The Collection 2008

This collection first published in 2007
by Express Newspapers
The Northern & Shell Building
10 Lower Thames Street
London EC3R 6EN

ISBN 978-0-85079340-6

Cover, internal design and reprographics by Dexter Graphics, Kent, UK

Printed and bound in China by SC International Ltd

The Collection 2008

Table of Contents:

An Introduction by

Martin Townsend

Every Christmas, when I was growing up, my mother would unfold a large and, as the years went by, increasingly tattered poster-sized cartoon and pin it up it in pride of place over our mantlepiece.

It showed a young, photography-mad Prince Andrew leaning out of a window of Buckingham Palace and taking pictures of a furious Santa Claus being menaced by the Queen's corgis.

That cartoon never failed to make us laugh. It was my first introduction to the work of Carl Giles, who has continued to make me laugh to this day.

For a budding young journalist his work was – and is – an object lesson in how to find humour and common humanity in great and sometimes grim events.

Giles fans all have their favourite characters – with ferocious Grandma usually top of the list. But I like the bit-part players too: from the urbane spivs and collapsed drunks to the hatchet-faced vicars and mewling babies. Then there are the settings: the cluttered front rooms and kitchens, the untidy suburban gardens, the fuggy saloon bars and down-at-heel seaside hotels.

It is almost a lost world now – but Giles immortalised it and the scenes remain as fresh and funny today as when they were first drawn. Indeed, when we decided to begin running a series of classic Giles cartoons in The Sunday Express magazine the post-bag from admiring readers was bigger than ever. Often imitated, never bettered, Giles remains the cartoonist's cartoonist. God bless him.

Martin Townsend
Editor, Sunday Express

Women and Men

"Like me to fill it in for you?"

Sunday Express, July 9, 1989

"I suppose this sudden urge to marry me couldn't have anything to do with Farmer's new £14,000,000 subsidy?"

Sunday Express, March 19, 1961

"Ole! Me and you cut off one side of the frontier, your mother and the kids the other."

Daily Express, June 10, 1969

"It's your own fault Mummy – you would keep rubbing it in about the R.A.C. saying women drivers are better than men."

Daily Express, May 22, 1969

"I only asked her what the Teachers' Union could teach her about the preparation for marriage and motherhood that I couldn't."

Sunday Express, April 24, 1960

"I'm not one of the hijackers; I'm keeping my wife covered in case she sings."

Daily Express, September 8, 1970

"It'll be interesting to see what they do when they come to Tibby."

Sunday Express, January 26, 1969

"First it was a Yank, then it was Adam Faith, then it was me,
now you want to marry a king."

Daily Express, May 4, 1961

"You'd better agree to a 'cooling off' period before you meet Bridget's latest boyfriend."

Sunday Express, April 23, 1972

"I'm not having a son of mine christened Apollo and that's final."

Daily Express, July 24, 1969

"I'll have a look at those when we get on board, Charles."

Daily Express, June 6, 1972

"'But you're already down under the scheme with four or five other young gents,' said a clerk of the London borough council which is guaranteeing engaged couples a house if they remain true to each other for three and a half years."

Daily Express, September 29, 1953

"Complications in this case present certain legal problems, your erring husband possessing no less than five 'Other Women' and three 'Other Wives'."

Daily Express, September 25, 1969

"Seen this, Romeo?"

Daily Express, November 7, 1961

"Not eating your brekky, dear? Worried who's next to get a public airing in Christine's biography?"

Daily Express, October 4, 1969

"Go tell Father Christmas that Mummy Christmas has come to join the office party."

Daily Express, December 22, 1970

"Married? Well, you just get straight back in there and get unmarried."

Sunday Express, September 19, 1954

"If we all watched where we were going instead of watching Sister Morgan's new uniform..."

Daily Express, May 14, 1970

"All right, Miss Linnet, I've got my lot covered - you can let yours out."

Sunday Express, March 8, 1964

"I wondered if you've got any ideas before my husband finds out that Horace here has eaten his Cup Final ticket."

Daily Express, May 4, 1971

"Advice to the Modern Girl - at the first sound of the word GOLF hand back his ring."

Sunday Express, February 9, 1969

"Horatio! You weren't watching the Round the Island Race at all. You were having a happening with those blasted hippies."

Daily Express, September 2, 1969

"Florrie - did you say that as it is Mothers' Day your husband was going to cook lunch while you had a game?"

Sunday Express, March 20, 1955

"Young people should take a cool detached look at each other's parents before committing themselves to a lifetime of marriage." *Getting Married* by B.M.A.

Daily Express, March 4, 1969

Religion

"Top of the Pops or not, daddy-o here just isn't with it."

Daily Express, November 24, 1960

"When I said I'd like to see more evidence of the 'Church Militant' in our little flock, I did not mean having three rounds with Mrs. Wilkins after morning service."

Sunday Express, August 24, 1969

"I would remind you that All Good Gifts Around Us have been carefully checked before the sermon."

Sunday Express, October 1, 1972

"Once again. This time we'll have the hymn version of 'All people that on earth do dwell' and not the Rugby Supporters' version - 'As I was walking through a wood'."

Sunday Express, January 16, 1972

"It's no good - it won't come off and he's on in ten minutes."

Sunday Express, March 12, 1989

"May we assume that we owe this honoured and most welcome visit to the possibility of your favourite TV Western going on strike?"

Sunday Express, February 12, 1961

"Agreeing with the Rev. Horace Spence who last week condemned children's' hymns as 'childish, sentimental or of introspective character', I offer the above illustration of some of the hymns he refers to."

A. All things bright and beautiful. B. You in your small corner. C. Fight the good fight.
D. We are but little children weak. E. Peace, perfect peace. F. Like a little candle.

Sunday Express, August 7, 1960

"Now the war is over I assume you have decided to risk the perils of travel and give us a look."

Sunday Express, March 3, 1991

"It was perhaps indiscreet to call her a heathen because she says she's going to watch the new TV series about Jesus."

Sunday Express, April 8, 1984

"If you accidentally put a pound coin in the kitty by mistake that's your bad luck mate!"

Sunday Express, November 18, 1984

Spot the 10 Differences

"Remember how we laughed at the Joneses for wasting their money going abroad with a lovely summer like this at home?"

Daily Express, July 30, 1959

"Remember how we laughed at the Joneses for wasting their money going abroad with a lovely summer like this at home?"

Daily Express, July 30, 1959

Children

"Stop pushing!"

Sunday Express, July 24, 1988

"Well, how did little Miss Bluit get on with her new class?"

Daily Express, January 10, 1961

"The Minister of Education, urging that **all** children from five to eleven should be sent to State schools said: 'Children of that age learning and playing together are not inhibited by any sense of differences'."

Daily Express, October 17, 1961

GILES AND BARKLEY GREET ST. GEORGE'S DAY

"Today, boys, I am going to read to you about St. George and the dragon."

Daily Express, April 23, 1953

"It's worth trying – didn't you read where a girl got suspended from school for wearing a beach suit this week?"

Sunday Express, November 21, 1954

"Stand by for squalls. Somebody is about to connect the empty chicken house with his Christmas dinner."

Daily Express, December 28, 1954

"Be brave, Miss Loris. Maybe the electricians will call off their strike tomorrow."

Daily Express, January 14, 1954

"You must make allowances for them getting bored with non-stop rain and Scrabble."

Sunday Express, August 11, 1985

The Sporting Life

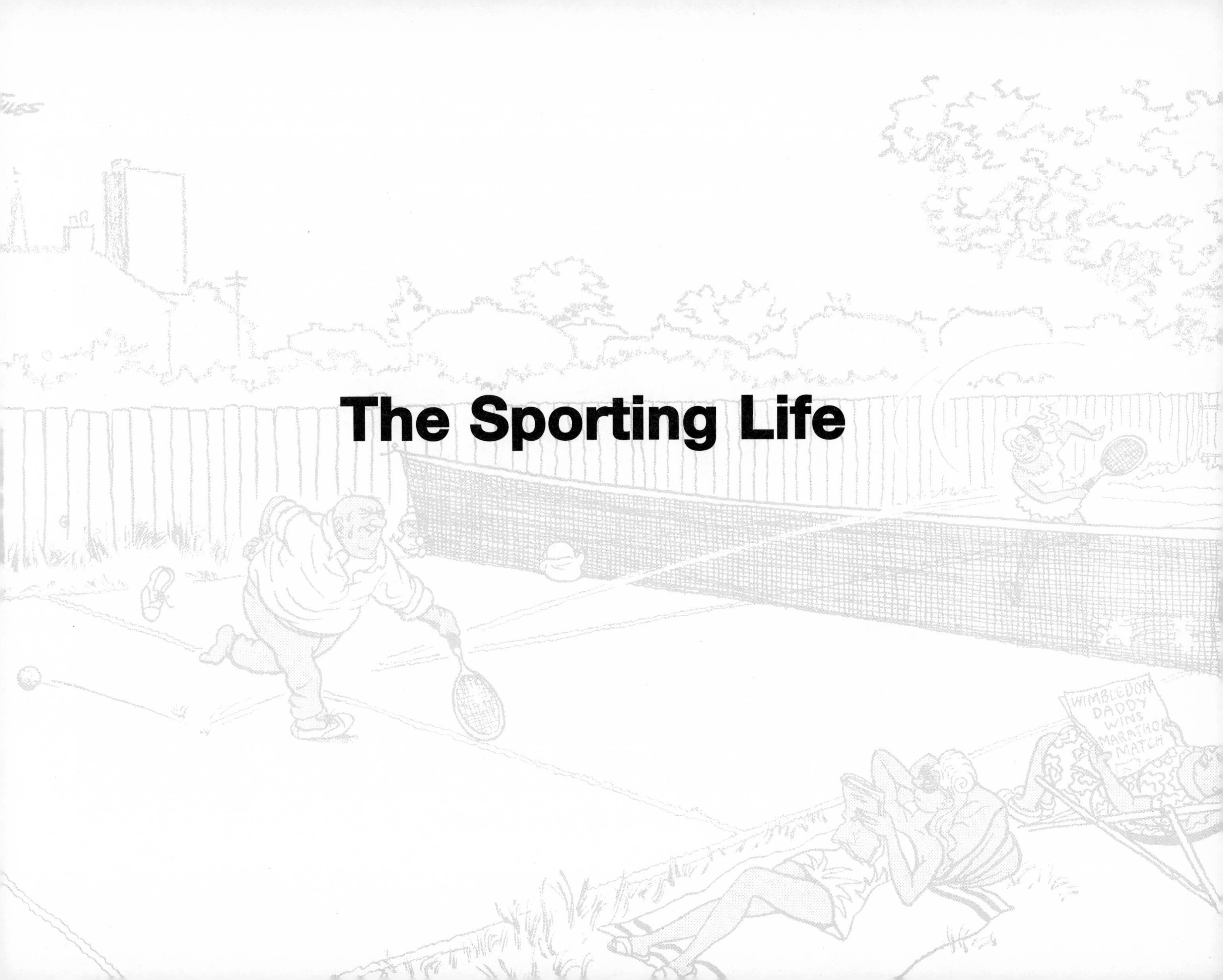

"Anybody here ride the last horse in the last race?"

Daily Express, March 22, 1960

"I don't think the Aussies quite liked the idea of being disqualified."

Daily Express, September 24, 1970

"I thinks it's a lovely name for a boy. But I still can't see why they have to christen it on the day of our last match of the season."

Sunday Express, September 5, 1971

"So far Hooliganism isn't identified with Ascot. But any more language like you've just used on your jockey and it'll be on the way."

Daily Express, June 14, 1988

"You can't hide yourself in there forever because you're a member of the Test Selectors Board."

Daily Express, July 7, 1988

"Actually, that double somersault by the Umpire when the ball caught his ankle was nothing to do with the brighter cricket promised by the M.C.C. "

Sunday Express, April 30, 1961

"Hark! Who's telling us the trouble with our Olympic team is that they don't train hard enough?"

Sunday Express, September 4, 1960

"I know what you're trying to do – you're trying to give me a cold so that I can part with my Cup replay ticket."

Daily Express, March 3, 1959

"Mr Rees – remember your statement to the Press that cricket was a dying game and will soon be replaced by Soccer as our national summer game?"

Daily Express, January 15, 1959

"From there to there – Test Matches. From there to there – Wimbledon. This week we have the British Open Gold Championship."

Daily Express, July 7, 1953

"When you asked if a few friends could come and listen to the fight from America, you didn't tell me it was three o'clock in the morning."

Daily Express, October 22, 1953

"Marvellous thing, football. All the summer we've been getting 'Can't take you and the children out today – it's raining'."

Sunday Express, August 15, 1954

"Tell Daddy some gentlemen are here to see him about the 50-1 Wimbledon to win the Cup he was giving them yesterday."

Sunday Express, May 15, 1988

"Not only trespassing but listening to a confounded band instead of cricket!"

Sunday Express, August 14, 1955

“Two items off the agenda this morning – Cheltenham and the state of the pitch in New Zealand.”

Daily Express, February 7, 1984

"I know he didn't. But it's good for trade."

Daily Express, January 13, 1971

"I distinctly saw a disbelieving frown when the Umpire ruled 'Not out'."

Sunday Express, May 2, 1971

"They must have given us the slip between the Arsenal ground and here."

Sunday Express, March 30, 1969

"Rodney! We are not at soccer."

Daily Express, March 25, 1969

"Hold it! That one you unanimously called him is definitely out."

Daily Express, November 18, 1969

"They moan all summer about the England cricketers, now they're moaning because the season's over."

Sunday Express, September 17, 1989

"I fear the great daddy of tennis in this family has been neglecting his winter training."

Daily Express, June 27, 1969

"Like last year, Butch, forget walkies for a few days after his marathon."

Daily Express, May 15, 1984

"Wasn't the one with the cap supposed to stop the ball going in the net?"

Sunday Express, January 8, 1961

"Keep your voice down, Grandma – the Colonel heard your remark: 'You don't mean to tell me South Africans actually pay money for our cricketers'."

Sunday Express, August 6, 1989

"Now there's a real fan – won't let a simple thing like the game being cancelled spoil his afternoon's sport."

Sunday Express, December 21, 1969

"Don't let him soften you up, Mac - get in there and give the umpires hell."

Daily Express, June 21, 1988

"Gentlemen! May I remind you that we are not playing soccer."

Sunday Express, June 11, 1972

"Apart from Idi Amin being kicked out of Queen's Tennis Club and McEnroe taking over Uganda, anything else happen while we were away?"

Daily Express July 30, 1985

"What kind of pep pills did you give him, Mulligan?"

Daily Express June 23, 1960

Spot the 10 Differences

"?"

Daily Express, April 15, 1965

"?"

Daily Express, April 15, 1965

Family Life

"'It is the easiest thing in the world for a child to detect that you're not really listening to him'... Marriage Guidance Council. *Especially if they can see your ear-plugs*."

Daily Express, June 20, 1969

"I hope not. Oh boy, I hope not."

Sunday Express, April 5, 1970

"Thanks for coming Uncle Joylon, and thanks for buying the children that lovely organ."

Daily Express, December 27, 1988

"Oh dear, they all left an hour ago – they thought they were staying with *you* for Christmas."

Sunday Express, December 24, 1989

"You go tell that judge that letting a man out for Christmas with his family is one thing – letting my family in to spend Christmas with me is another."

Daily Express, December 22, 1961

"Stand by for tidings of good cheer from the neighbours – Dad's just blown every fuse in the road."

Sunday Express, December 11, 1988

"Two miles from the Scottish border and first you tell me you don't drink Scotch and then you tell me you don't like haggis!"

Scottish Daily Express, September 6, 1954

"Women win with right to work until 65 – round here they let you work till you're 165 for free."

Daily Express, April 3, 1986

Public Transport

"I read that Khrushchev has told the Russians at the British Trade Fair not to believe that we all go to work by Rolls-Royce."

Daily Express, May 23, 1961

"That'll teach 'em to write slogans on our coaches."

Daily Express, February 11, 1953

"Bus strike or no bus strike, I'll get the next lot that take a quick cut across my garden to the station."

Sunday Express, October 17, 1954

"You ought to be ashamed – kicking their little trains all over the place just because you had to walk home."

Sunday Express, June 5, 1955

"He does that every time British Rail put their fares up."

Sunday Express, November 24, 1985

"I don't know what the Queen's moaning about. Forty-five minutes delay and no restaurant service is norm on our line."

Daily Express, February 6, 1986

The Long Arm of the Law

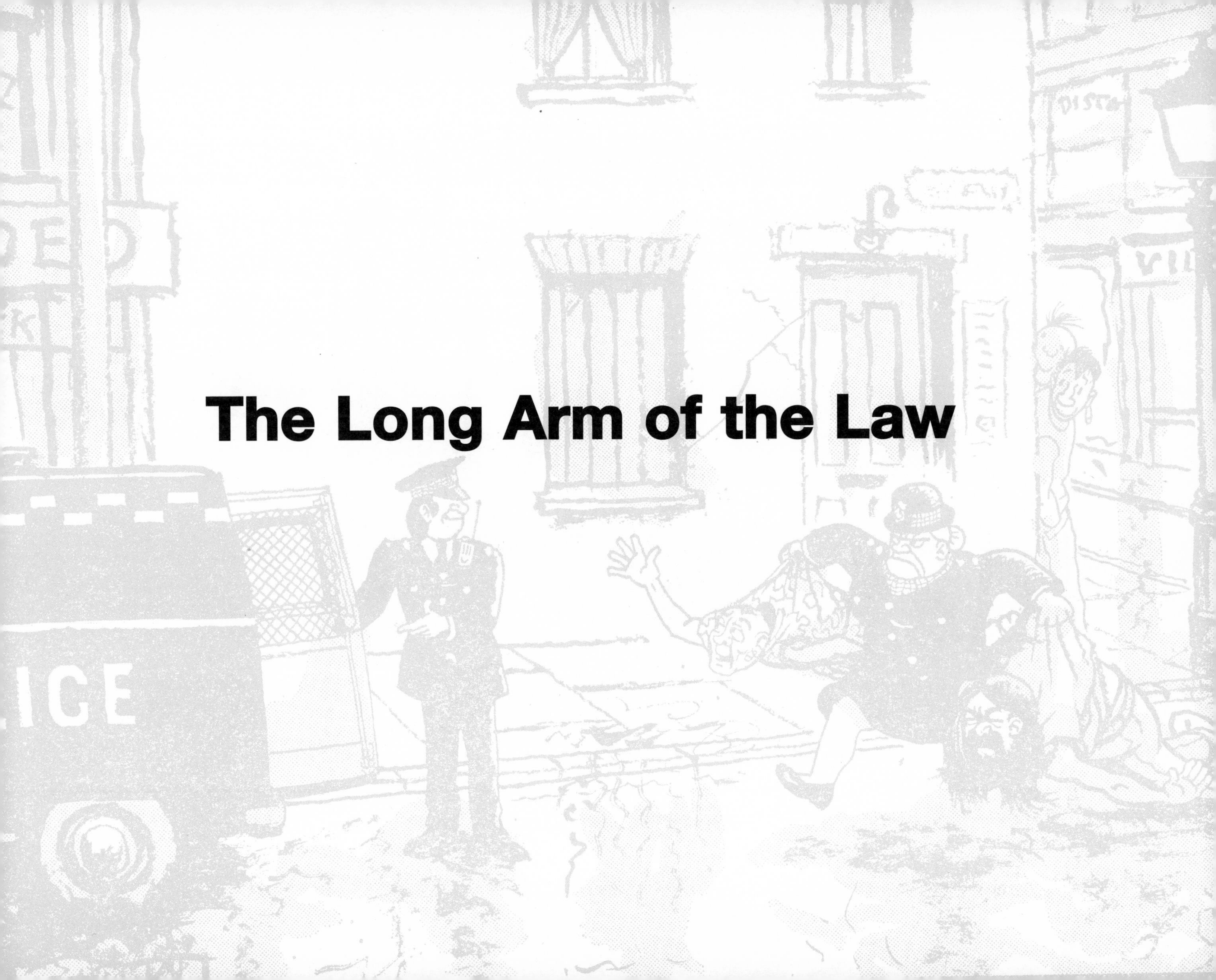

"We're parked on a double yellow line."

Daily Express, December 29, 1970

"Just leave it there one minute over time my lad – that's all."

Daily Express, February 7, 1961

"The one that keeps going Ho! Ho! Ho! is the owner."

Daily Express, December 3, 1959

"Closing the court because a lady shorthand writer wants to get home and get to bed is one thing – granting a similar request on behalf of the defendant is another, Mr Birdfoot."

Daily Express, November 14, 1961

"I am aware of Lord Goodman's opinion that the British Legal System is 'Demented'; nevertheless this boy did wilfully commit the serious crime of acquiring sixpenny worth of sweets after legal shopping hours."

Sunday Express, September 27, 1970

"Madam would go a long way towards improving her public relationship with the police if she would kindly remove her car from my foot."

Daily Express, November 20, 1959

"Never mind about Big Brother – Big Sister has been watching you ... illegally parking since eight o'clock."

Daily Express, January 3, 1984

"A constable may soon arrest without warrant anyone whom he believes to be carrying an offensive weapon; an offensive weapon is defined as 'any article made or adapted to cause injury, or intended by the person having it for such use'."

Sunday Express, February 14, 1953

"I only said, 'You wouldn't happen to be one of those Kiss-o-gram cops?'."

Daily Express, November 26, 1985

"Silent night..."

Sunday Express, December 16, 1956

Politics and Government

"Hold tight, sir."

Daily Express, March 30, 1971

“Kidnapping Mr Lawson won’t cut the mortgages – he’ll only be another mouth to feed. Take him back.”

Sunday Express, October 8, 1989

"Frankly, young man, I do NOT recall patting your head in the last election and whispering I'd abolish schools if your father voted for me."

Daily Express, September 24, 1959

"Watch this M.P. pick my brother up – we've painted him all over with treacle."

Sunday Express, April 24, 1955

"If we went where they told us, at least we shouldn't be getting snow in May."

Daily Express, May 19, 1955

"I like the way they tell how they're going to grind their opponents in the dust in the same breath that they ask you to elect them as a 'man of peace'."

Daily Express, April 26, 1955

Spot the 10 Differences

"?"

Daily Express, April 15, 1965

"?"

Daily Express, April 15, 1965

Royalty

SOUTHAMPTON
A Port Office & DOCKS
TOWN QUAY ROYAL PIER & FERRY
HIPPY FESTIVAL ISLE OF WIGHT
MAKE LUV

"I hardly feel, dear, that because the sink at Balmoral hasn't been working properly since your great-great-grandmother's time, it justifies claiming a rent rebate."

Daily Express, November 5, 1970

"Thought you'd take the micky out of the Guards in last week's Sunday Express then hop off out of the country for a while, did you?"

Sunday Express, May 24, 1953

"Philip, did you telephone the council about this new rent assistance bill?"

Daily Express, July 15, 1971

"If HRH puts her horse down in that puddle once more, HRH is going to lose quite a lot of my goodwill."

Sunday Express, October 29, 1972

"That's great, Ma'am. Thanks for the lift."

Daily Express, August 27, 1970

"Nothing gets on my nerves more than a bailiff whistling Elgar's 'Pomp and Circumstance'."

Daily Express, November 11, 1969

The Military

"Cigarette, anyone?"

Sunday Express, April 25, 1954

"I'm sure war's not as imminent as all that, Grandma."

Daily Express, February 1, 1955

"Fast as I tell him to 'See 'em off', they tell him to 'Sit'."

Sunday Express, December 10, 1961

"Can't have us all becoming skilled overnight, can we?"

Daily Express, March 4, 1954

"If you will run on about how many Messerschmitts you shot down during the Battle of Britain in front of our German au pair girl..."

Sunday Express, September 17, 1972

"Mum can't find your tin hat, but she doesn't think you'll meet with a lot of flak between here and the pub."

Sunday Express, September 3, 1989

"Bye, honey - Sergeant's going to make your loved one look like Gregory Peck."

Daily Express, December 9, 1954

"British Air Ministry? You know those three girl diplomats you sent to encourage G.I.s to like Britain? Well, they've married three G.I.s and gone to live in the States."

Sunday Express, October 24, 1954

Spot the 10 Differences

"?"

Daily Express, April 15, 1965

"?"

Daily Express, April 15, 1965

Spot the 10 differences – the answers

FISH TEAS
inkle Specials
ICES
NO SINGING
CAFE FULL

LIVE AMMO
KEEP OUT
SPEND YOUR HOLIDAY WITH THE T.A. JOIN TODAY!
FALL IN
NEW ARRIVALS
IN
CHANGE HERE AND CLOCK IN
CHANGE HERE AND CLOCK OUT
OUT
WOMENS' QTS
NO ADMITTANCE EXCEPT ON BUSINESS
THAT REPORT
GILES

LIVE AMMO
KEEP OUT
SPEND YOUR HOLIDAY WITH THE
JOIN TODAY!
NEW ARRIVALS
IN
CHANGE HERE AND CLOCK IN
CHANGE HERE AND CLOCK OUT
OUT
WOMENS' QTS
NO ADMITTANCE
EXCEPT ON BUSINESS
GILES

SEE THE SUN
200 francs
HUILE POUR BRUNIR
GLACES
DU
SOLEIL
TRAITEMENT du SOLEIL
SUN-RAY TREAT.
GILES

SEE THE SUN
00 francs
HUILE POUR BRUNIR
PROMENAD
DU SOLEIL
TRAITEMENT du SOLEIL
SUN-RAY TREAT.
GILES

BILLIARDS
RESTAURANT
POLO
RULE 1 DON'T FALL OFF
DANCE
SWIMMING POOL
TENNIS RULES
PUTTING GREEN
RULES
HOAMLEIGH LTD
HOLIDAY CAMP
NOT ANOTHER CAMP LIKE IT
RAMBLE
FALL IN HERE
TO THE SEA
43 MILES
Escape Route
GILES

RESTAURANT
BILLIARDS
DE DANCE
SWIMMING POOL
TENNIS RULES
POLO
RULE 1
DON'T FALL OFF
PUTTING GREEN
RULES
HOAMLEIGH
HOLIDAY CAM
NOT ANOTHER CAMP LIKE IT
RAMBLE
FALL IN HERE
TO THE SEA
43 MILES
Escape Route
GILES